Peter Stanier is the author of 'Discover Dorset': *The Industrial Past*, which includes a chapter on mills. He was born in Cornwall and now lives in Shaftesbury, Dorset, where he is a freelance lecturer and writer on archaeology, industrial archaeology and landscapes. Peter read archaeology and geography at Southampton University, where he later received a doctorate. His main field of research is stone quarrying, on which he has published both papers and books. He is editor of the Association for Industrial Archaeology's quarterly *Industrial Archaeology News*. His other books include *Quarries and Quarrying* (1985), *Dorset's Industrial Heritage* (1989) and *Quarries of England and Wales* (1995).

Following page
Steve Northover using a mill bill to dress a millstone at Randall's or Grove Mill, Burton Bradstock, in about 1935. This was a regular task that every miller had to perform.

DISCOVER DORSET

MILLS

PETER STANIER

THE DOVECOTE PRESS

Sturminster Newton Mill.

First published in 2000 by The Dovecote Press Ltd
Stanbridge, Wimborne, Dorset BH21 4JD

ISBN 1 874336 72 5

© Peter Stanier 2000

Peter Stanier has asserted his rights under the Copyright, Designs
and Patent Act 1988 to be identified as author of this work

Series designed by Humphrey Stone

Typeset in Monotype Sabon
Printed and bound by Baskerville Press, Salisbury, Wiltshire

A CIP catalogue record for this book is available
from the British Library

1 3 5 7 9 8 6 4 2

CONTENTS

INTRODUCTION 8

A SHORT HISTORY 10

WATER AND WHEELS 15

THE CORN MILL AT WORK 21

COUNTRY MILLS 30

TOWN MILLS 36

INDUSTRIAL MILLS 41

FARM WHEELS 48

WINDMILLS 52

HORSE MILLS 57

TURBINES 59

MILLWRIGHTS AND WHEEL MAKERS 61

WATER PUMPING 63

WORKING COMMERCIAL MILLS 65

MILLS OPEN TO THE PUBLIC 70

FURTHER READING 78

ACKNOWLEDGEMENTS 79

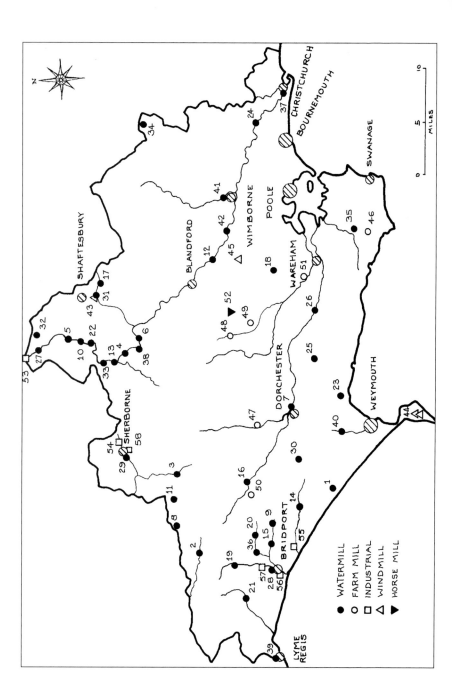

DORSET MILLS MENTIONED IN THE TEXT

CORN MILLS

1	Abbotsbury	SY 578851
2	Buckham	ST 471049
3	Chetnole	ST 604081
4	Cut	ST 776165
5	Eccliffe	ST 798253
6	Fiddleford	ST 801136
7	Fordington	SY 699906
8	Halstock	ST 531086
9	Hembury	SY 526931
10	High Bridge	ST 790229
11	Holt	ST 570089
12	Keynston	ST 914035
13	Kings	ST 766172
14	Litton Cheney	SY 550904
15	Loders	SY 498941
16	Maiden Newton	SY 596977
17	Melbury Abbas	ST 877207
18	Morden	SY 906939
19	Netherbury	SY 472993
20	Powerstock	SY 505963
21	Stoke	SY 424973
22	Stour Provost	ST 791215
23	Sutton Poyntz	SY 706837
24	Throop	SZ 113958
25	Warmwell	SY 749873
26	Water Barn	SY 832873
27	Waterloo	ST 788295
28	West, Bridport	SY 463931
29	West, Sherborne	ST 632154
30	Winterbourne Steepleton	SY 628899

WORKING MILLS

31	Cann	ST 872208
32	Purns	ST 807281
33	Stalbridge West	ST 756192

MILLS OPEN

34	Alderholt	SU 119143
35	Boar	SU 961822
36	Mangerton	SY 490957
37	Place	SZ 160924
38	Sturminster Newton	ST 782135
39	Town, Lyme Regis	SY 342922
40	Upwey	SY 663851
41	Walford	SU 009007
42	White	ST 958006

WINDMILL/SITES

43	Cann	ST 872208
44	Easton north, Portland	SY 691714
44	Easton south, Portland	SY 692713
45	'Windmill Barrow'	SY 937977

FARM MILLS

46	Blashenwell	SY 951803
47	Forston	SY 666955
48	Hewish	ST 806001
49	Roke	SY 835960
50	Toller Fratrum	SY 578973
51	Trigon	SY 884886

HORSE MILL

52	Winterborne Whitechurch	SY 840997

INDUSTRIAL

53	Bourton Foundry	ST 775310
54	Castleton water pump	ST 646169
55	Grove	SY 490897
56	Old Brewery	SY 465921
57	Pymore	SY 470946
58	Sherborne, silk	ST 635159

INTRODUCTION

The term 'mill' comes from the Latin *molinum* or Old English *mylen*, which means to grind, as in the case of corn milling, although it has come to refer to any site where machinery is used for manufacturing purposes.

Dorset's many rivers and streams have powered a great number and variety of watermills since at least Saxon times, and continue to do so today. Because water is so readily available, the application of wind power was never widespread, although a small number of windmills have been recorded from the thirteenth century until the 1890s. Tidemills, exploiting the rise and fall of the tides, were recorded in 1590 at Melcombe Regis and Weymouth in a sale of a 'plat pece of grounde, and Arme of the Sea Milles thereupon erected.' To a much lesser extent, horse-worked mills were of local importance.

The main function of watermills sited on streams was for grinding corn – as befits an agricultural county – but there were instances when water power was applied to different functions, including brewing, farmwork, fulling cloth, sawmills, textiles, paper making and water-pumping.

It is sometimes surprising to find a watermill sited close to the source of even the smallest stream, which is explained by the plentiful flow springing from the natural reservoirs within the chalk downs and limestone hills. Such a wheel might have operated only for an hour or two until the mill pond emptied, but there was usually sufficient power for farm mills which worked intermittently.

At some mills the traditional water wheels were replaced by more efficient water turbines from the 1880s onwards, in a drive to increase efficiency in the face of larger competitors. Occasionally, steam power was applied at larger mills, with oil and gas engines also being used.

Mills in Dorset have been recorded in different ways over the centuries, during which time the county boundary has changed.

'Domesday Book' of 1086 was the first significant survey, recording around 277 'mills', but it was not until the Napoleonic wars at the close of the eighteenth century that a survey concerned with the defence of the county recorded 164 watermills and two windmills. Trade directories indicate the number of millers and mills at work in the nineteenth and early twentieth centuries.

In the second half of the twentieth century, several surveys were made to record the state of surviving mills and/or the sites of earlier mills. L. Abbott, the County Planning Officer, recorded at least 144 watermills or mill sites in 1952, of which 11 were still working as corn mills and 9 others had miscellaneous functions, including electricity generation. Eight years later, a summary of this list was published in H.S.L. Dewar's discussion of Dorset water, wind and horse-mills. A more detailed survey was carried out in the 1960s by Joseph Addison, who recorded at least 204 mill sites (157 watermills, 35 farm wheels, 6 industrial mills and 6 pumping wheels), with an indication of a further 32 sites. Addison included measured drawings of some of the wheels and his photographic record is preserved in the Dorset County Museum, Dorchester. The last county-wide survey was made in the 1980s for Dorset County Council. This unpublished report, which combined documentary, map and field evidence, suggested the existence of at least 400 mill sites in Dorset, although only about half would have been working at any one time.

This book sets out to explain the nature of Dorset's mills and, in particular, the evidence found today. There are mills surviving with machinery either in working order or derelict condition; others have been converted to housing or industrial purposes; those demolished have left but the slightest clue. Measurements of wheels etc, are given in feet and inches, as they were current at the time of building.

Most of the sites mentioned in the text can be seen, at the very least, from a public road or footpath, but they are all private property and their inclusion here should not imply the right of entry; however, a polite request to visit is seldom denied. Mills open to the public are described at the end of the book.

A SHORT HISTORY

The basic process of grinding grain into flour dates back to the first Neolithic farmers who used a saddle quern, a hard stone with a smooth curved surface upon which the grain was ground by hand with a smaller 'rubber' stone. With the introduction of the hand rotary quern in the Iron Age we see something more recognisable as a 'millstone'. Rotary querns had two circular stones, each with a flat surface. The top 'runner' stone was turned by an attached wooden handle and rotated on a wooden spindle fixed to the centre of the bedstone. Grain was poured in through a hole in the centre and ground between the two stones. These stones or their fragments have been excavated at settlement sites, such as Gussage All Saints, from where a bedstone of a rotary quern and part of a saddle quern are now displayed in the Dorset County Museum. Hard and gritty sandstones were particularly suitable for querns.

The Romans are said to have introduced the water mill into Britain, but there is no evidence for them in Dorset. Early mills had horizontal wheels but the Roman 'Vitruvian' undershot wheel could turn a millstone through gearing. It is clear there were watermills in Dorset in Saxon times. Some may have been without gearing, having instead a direct drive to a millstone from a small horizontal wheel with paddles or 'tirls' to harness the water. These were similar to the 'Norse mills' which survive in Shetland, Orkney and Lewis - very small scale but easy to work. Others had vertical waterwheels of the undershot type with simple gearing to drive a single pair of stones. Saxon mills were probably all built of timber on a stone foundation. A rare timber structure excavated in 1988 at Worgret near Wareham may have been a Saxon watermill, possibly dating from the late seventh or early eighth century. It could have been for corn milling or iron production, or possibly both. The wheel may even have been an overshot type. In the absence of other physical evidence, two early charters refer to mills. In 933 AD Athelstan granted Sherborne Abbey a property at Bradford Abbas 'audlang lace to Mylenburnham' ('along the slow stream to the Millbourne'), and in 1019, Cnut granted Agemund 16 hides in Cheselbourne 'bi streme in thane Milliere' ('from the bed by the stream by the mill weir'?).

'Domesday Book' (1086) gives the first overall picture of the extent of mills in Dorset; all those listed were, in effect, established Saxon mills. Each mill site would have included a waterwheel with a pair of gears driving a single pair of millstones. It has been suggested that some were animal-powered because their sites lack a water supply today, but it is likely that the water table was higher in the eleventh century. There are around 277 mills listed in 'Domesday Book', owned by 178 manors. Forty-three manors held between two and four mills each, while some held a fraction of a mill, such as Worgret which was divided equally between Cerne Abbey and William de Briouze. In the Blackmore Vale area of the upper Stour and its tributaries there were as many as 44 mills. These included three mills worth 40s held by Glastonbury Abbey at 'Newentone' (Sturminster Newton). Land held in the Vale by Shaftesbury Abbey included a mill worth 10s at 'Haintone' (Hinton St Mary), three mills worth 30s at 'Sture' (Stour), three mills worth 11s 7d at 'Fontemale' (Fontmell Magna), a mill worth 50d at 'Contone' (Compton Abbas), four mills worth 15s 3d at Melbury Abbas, three mills worth 17s at 'Euneminstre' (Iwerne Minster) and a mill worth 5s at 'Fifhead' (Fifehead).

During the medieval period tenants were obliged to take their grain for grinding at their local mill which was owned by the Lord of the Manor. Hand mills were illegal. This was known as the milling 'soke', by which the miller usually took payment in the form of a percentage of the corn ground for the manor. There were cases of unscrupulous and dishonest millers who abused the system and harmed the reputation of millers as a whole, most famously in the character of Chaucer's miller in The Canterbury Tales: 'He was a master-hand at stealing grain./ He felt it with his hand and thus he knew/ Its quality and took three times his due.' The system lasted until at least the seventeenth century, but it was not until an Act of 1796 that millers could charge a fee for their work.

An important medieval mill is that of the Benedictine Abbey at

The remains of the medieval Abbey Mill at Abbotsbury. Its two internal waterwheels were behind the arch, where the wheelpits survive today.

Abbotsbury, which survives as a stone building known as the Old Malthouse immediately east of the Abbey church, now in the grounds of the Abbey House Guest House. Archaeological investigations in 1984-85 located an earlier building beneath. The fourteenth-century mill was built with good stone masonry, with a central archway and a wide chamber with room for two vertical overshot waterwheels, each to drive a pair of millstones. There was certainly one wheel in use, and scratch marks in the wheel pit suggest it was up to 13ft diameter. After the Dissolution in 1539, the buildings were sold and it is believed that a single smaller waterwheel (about 12ft diameter and 2ft wide) was installed to work a single pair of stones. The mill continued in use until the mid-eighteenth century.

It may seem surprising that Abbotsbury had a mill. A charter of 1024 refers to the 'mylenbroc' (mill stream) for mills at Abbotsbury and Portesham. When Abbot William Cerne died in 1401 his lands included 'one watermill worth yearly 3s 4d and not more because in summer they cannot grind for want of water.' This illustrates the problem of harnessing a small stream so near its source. Conditions further upstream at Portesham must have been even worse. By 1593 there were two other mills recorded downstream: a corn mill and a fulling mill. In 1662 a lease of Abbey and Lower Mills was granted to Thomas Ham who was required to repair and maintain the 'Houses, Walls, Mill stones, Mill wheeles, Coggs, Roungs, Beeles, Spindells, Trendells, Iron stuffe, Implements, Necessarie waters, Watercourses, Ponds, Timber workes.' It is believed that the Abbey Mill had closed by 1740 when the Lower Mill (where the miller chose to live) became known as the Abbey Mill. Of nine millstone fragments found at Abbotsbury, three were old red sandstone, one was basaltic lava, while five were burr-stones of a much later date.

While much of interest was recovered at Abbotsbury, excavations in 1972-73 were less conclusive at the grassed-over site of Daw's Mill high on a tributary of the Frome near Benville Bridge. The mill building was not found, but loose stones and a great number of nails implied it was of timber. Sherds of poorly made pottery suggest that miller Ellis Daw and his successors at the end of the seventeenth century were 'not particularly affluent.' Another site with some remaining earthworks and a scatter of medieval and later pottery is Hogford Mill on the River Allen at Pamphill, near Wimborne. In this case there are records in the Kingston Lacy Estate accounts. 'Hoggefordmull' is first recorded in 1380-1, when it was held by John and Edith Samford. A fulling mill had been built by 1408 when John Forster was tenant. The site appears to have declined by the early seventeenth century and had been abandoned by 1774.

Although they may be on earlier sites, most mills seen today date from the latest rebuilding from the eighteenth century onwards. By the beginning of the century extra gearing had been introduced, enabling two or more pairs of stones to be driven from a wheel. This was also a period which saw a rise in population and the onset of industrialisation. In its wake came technological improvements to water and wind power; many mills took advantage of the advances made in design. Prominent engineers of the time, such as John Rennie and John Smeaton, turned their minds to the problem of improving the efficiency of water and wind power.

By the 1880s, water turbines had made an appearance in Dorset and were found to be efficient and trouble-free, many being made and installed by the Ringwood engineer Joseph J. Armfield. In the nineteenth century steam power was applied to new roller milling machinery at the larger mills, especially in towns and ports. Fordington Mill at Dorchester is an example entirely rebuilt and modernised in 1892. This new form of power meant that steam milling could take place anywhere and was no longer restricted to a site beside a water course. It was the larger steam roller mills that brought about the decline of small rural water mills. The larger mills were located at ports through which grain was increasingly imported from North America. Railways and then motor lorries could carry more and travel further than horse-drawn wagons, and thus enterprising mills expanded their markets at the expense of the smaller mills. Gas and oil engines were also installed to supplement water power.

Trade directories from the early nineteenth century until 1939 list millers within Dorset's county boundary of the time. Information taken from *Kelly's Directories* at selected dates suggests the number of mills and millers as follows:

YEAR:	1855	1875	1885	1895	1911	1923	1939
MILLERS:	148	138	122	120	88	61	37

Although smaller farm mills are excluded, the figures clearly indicate the decline of corn mills, while the details show the rise of a few larger milling firms from the turn of the nineteenth century. It was around the time of the Second World War that more mills ceased working and they continued to decline rapidly thereafter.

Today, Cann Mills near Shaftesbury is the only commercial water-powered corn mill left. In the same area of north Dorset, the premises at Purn's Mill and Stalbridge West Mill are used to produce animal feeds. There are preserved watermills, some producing a little flour, open to the public at Alderholt, Lyme Regis (Town Mill), Mangerton, Sturminster Marshall (White Mill) and Sturminster Newton.

WATER AND WHEELS

Most early mills were sited beside a river, where their wheels were turned directly by the passing flow. The advantages of a head (height) of water could be achieved by hatches placed across a stream above the mill, but weirs and leats became more common in time. A weir built across a river or stream, when combined with hatches, not only raised the head of water but also helped regulate the flow. A leat (artificial channel) dug from a weir enabled the mill to be sited away from the river bank, in a more convenient position, and perhaps a short distance down the valley to increase the head of water. Hatches or sluices control the amount of water entering the leat from the weir, being lowered to hold back water and raised to allow excess water to flow out beneath. Leats bringing water to the mill from a spring or stream vary in length from a few feet to a mile or so, according to the steepness of the river valley, property boundaries or other factors.

If one source was inadequate, water was sometimes taken from more than one supply. For example, Upwey Mill is supplied by a leat

The iron trough of the aqueduct to the farm wheel at Toller Fratrum brought water from a source half-a-mile away, crossing a sunken lane.

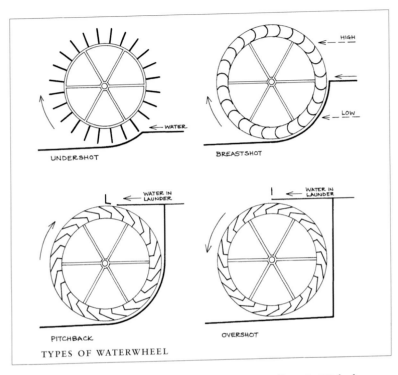

UNDERSHOT   BREASTSHOT

WATER

HIGH

LOW

WATER IN LAUNDER

PITCHBACK   OVERSHOT

TYPES OF WATERWHEEL

and a stream, a wheel at Magiston Farm near Sydling St Nicholas was worked from leats from Sydling Water and a second source, while the Castleton waterwheel at Sherborne utilised water from three streams.

A number of farm wheels were erected close to springs, if the flow of water provided enough power. At Blashenwell Farm near Corfe Castle, spring water was collected in a pond behind a dam and the water conveyed underground to a vertical pipe and a cast-iron pentrough to give a head of about 4ft, although apparently never very successful. The millpond and mill site at Lulworth Cove are close to a good spring. Springhead, near Fontmell Magna, is another instance where a millpond is fed by springs.

A millpond behind a dam increases the available head of water and preserves enough water for a day's working. This was especially important when using a small stream or spring, such as at Melbury Abbas and Cann Mill. At Purn's Mill, Gillingham, a wide leat diverted from the stream doubles up as a millpond.

Melbury Abbas Mill, a rural mill in North Dorset with an iron overshot wheel made by E.S. Hindley of Bourton in 1875 and fed from a millpond.

At the mill itself a hatch controls the speed of the waterwheel, and can be operated by the miller from within the building. The hatch is usually raised to let water under to the waterwheel, although a variation is the depressing sluice (an idea invented by John Rennie in the 780s). This is kept raised when the mill is not in use, so that waste water flows out beneath, but when the sluice is lowered (i.e. depressed) the water ponds up behind it before overflowing onto the wheel. This has an advantage of increasing the head of water operating on the wheel.

The tailrace is another consideration, for it is important to ensure there is no ponding-back to impede the turning of the waterwheel. Tail water is normally returned straight to the stream, but sometimes this is not always possible. The farm wheel at Forston, for example, took water from the River Cerne but required a long tailrace across a field before the water could be returned to the river at the correct level downstream.

The power of a waterwheel depends on its diameter and width as well as the availability and head of water. The simplest type of vertical waterwheel is known as an undershot and has floatboards like paddles which are turned by the action of a stream flowing past where there is little head of water available. With increasing head, the weight of the water can be used to turn a wheel more efficiently by filling buckets

Maiden Newton has an external 16ft by 10ft breastshot wheel made by
Winter & Hossey of Dorchester.

fitted fitted between shrouds. The wheel becomes a low breastshot,
then a breastshot when the water enters half way up the wheel, or a
high breastshot wheel when water is introduced at about three-
quarters height. Full use can be made of the water if it is brought in at
full height, when the wheel is known as a pitchback, or an overshot if
the water is fed over the top of the wheel so that it turns forwards.
Water is directed onto a high breastshot, pitchback or overshot wheel
in a trough called a launder.

Early timber wheels were of the 'compass arm' type, with four arms

The spectacular 60 ft waterwheel at Bourton Foundry, built in 1837, was a local landmark for many years, until it was demolished in 1918. The wheelpit remains today.

fastened to a wheel shaft (axle) by mortise and tenon joints, which weakened the wheel and limited its size. Much stronger and larger wheels were built partly or entirely of iron. Firstly, iron wheel shafts were introduced at the end of the eighteenth century, followed in the next century by iron wheels with shrouds (rims), arms (spokes) and buckets. The wheel shaft, which may be square or octagonal, provides the main drive but an alternative is the suspension wheel which has a ring gear drive and a small pinion wheel attached to a lay shaft. This type has the advantage of increasing the take-off speed while also relieving the strain on the wheel's shaft and arms so they can be of lighter construction.

Most surviving wheels are made of iron, either entirely or sometimes with wooden arms. With undershot or low breastshot wheels the wooden floats can be easily replaced when damaged or rotted. For other wheels the shrouds are iron, with buckets of iron or wood. According to their design buckets can be L- or J-shaped, while 'ventilated' buckets fill more efficiently because small holes allow trapped air to escape.

There was a spectacular high breastshot wheel at Bourton Foundry measuring 60ft diameter and 2ft wide, erected in 1837 and dismantled in 1918. But diameter was not everything, where it could be made up in width. In west Dorset, an iron breastshot wheel at Pymore measured 7ft 6in diameter and 6ft wide. The mill burnt out in 1959 and the wheel was removed, although the wheel pit remains. East Mill, Bridport, had an iron wheel just 8ft diameter but 8ft wide installed in 1865. In contrast, some very small waterwheels were installed locally, often for water pumping, such as one of 6ft diameter by ft 0in wide at Frampton Court and Farm.

The two largest wheels surviving in Dorset today are the 26ft diameter by 3ft 9in wide wheel at the Castleton water pumping station, Sherborne, and a farm wheel of 26ft diameter by 2ft 2in wide at Toller Fratrum. The wheel remaining at Maiden Newton Mill is an impressive 6ft diameter by 0ft wide. The earliest dated iron wheel in Dorset (Maggs, Bourton, 1819) is a breastshot wheel 7ft diameter by 7ft 9in wide from Nether Cerne Manor Farm. The surviving half of this wheel is now displayed at the Castleton pumping station, Sherborne.

THE CORN MILL AT WORK

A typical corn or grist mill may also include the miller's house, either attached or standing close by. The common mill arrangement has three floors: the ground or machinery floor, the stone floor where the milling takes place and the bin floor above. The vertical waterwheel is in a wheelpit inside or outside the mill building. At the end of the wheel shaft a large geared pit wheel engages with the wallower attached to the main upright shaft which extends up through the mill. Upright shafts were originally of timber with an iron gudgeon at the bottom supported on a beam or sprattle which could be adjusted for position. Later examples are supported by a cast-iron arch which gives better access to the wheel shaft bearing. The great spur wheel on the upright shaft provides the drive for the millstones on the first floor. A small cogged pinion, the stone nut, is engaged with the spur wheel to turn the spindle which passes up through a hole in the centre of the bed stone to the rynd which supports and drives the runner stone. This

Mill gearing at Alderholt Mill: the pit wheel (rear), with the great spur wheel (top), wallower, and upright shaft suuported on an iron arch.

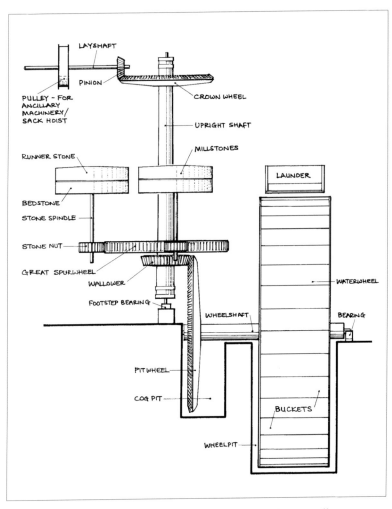

The machinery for a typical water-powered corn mill

is known as underdrift milling. The speed is greatly increased when transferred from the outside of the great spur wheel to the stone nut, giving a preferred speed of about 130-140 rpm for the runner stone. In practice, two or more stones can be driven from stone nuts and the great spur wheel. A jack ring and screw is the usual method of lowering or raising the stone nut in and out of mesh with the spur wheel.

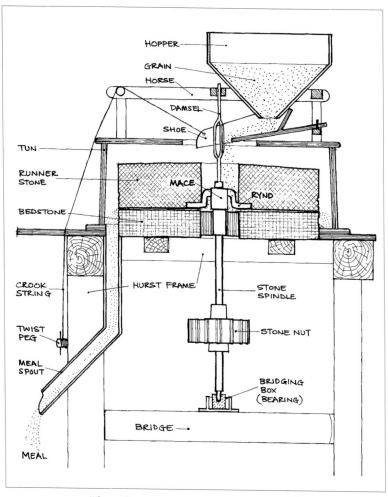

The millstone arrangement for a corn mill.
D = damsel   M = mace   R = rynd or bridge

The upright shaft, in constant motion when the waterwheel is turning, can be engaged to work other equipment. The crown wheel, for example, may drive the sack hoist to lift sacks of grain to the bins in the top or attic floor of the mill. The most common sack hoist has a slack belt which becomes tight to engage with a turning pulley wheel when a chain or rope is pulled from any floor in the mill. Hoists

A close view showing the rare all-timber gearing at White
Mill, near Sturminster Marshall, with the great spur wheel
and wallower on the right, and the pit wheel, left.
Although no longer working, this historic machinery
has been conserved by the National Trust.

outside the mill building are usually protected from the weather by a
boarded lucam; if inside the mill, sack traps in the floor close
automatically once the sack has passed up through. Elevators can be
used to move grain around the mill to where it is required and may
even replace sack hoists.

Mill gearing became more sophisticated after the late seventeenth
century, so that more than one pair of stones could be driven. White

Mill on the Stour is of special interest because it contains all-wooden gearing dating from the eighteenth century. Most geared wheels seen today are cast-iron but have been mortised to take cogs of hardwoods such as apple or hornbeam, while oak is preferred for the pit wheel where it is constantly wet. Should anything go wrong, wooden cogs will tear out rather than cause serious damage if the whole machinery jammed. They are relatively easy to replace when they become worn or damaged. Pulleys and belts are an alternative to gearing, and can be seen at the turbine-powered Sturminster Newton Mill.

Grain or grist is ground and reduced to meal between two stones set close together. As the top runner stone rotates, the pattern dressed on the face of both stones moves the grain fed in at the central eye towards the outside edge for grinding before spilling out as meal into the vat. The art of dressing millstones dates back to Roman times. The usual pattern has segments or harps made up of furrows and lands, the latter dressed with thin groves called stitching. A few composite millstones were 'sickle dresed', in a series of curved lands and furrows, without being grouped into segments. There is said to be no great advantage although they may grind a little faster.

The usual millstone sizes were from 3ft 6in to 4ft diameter but stones 5ft 6in diameter have been recorded. An ideal arrangement was to have three pairs of stone,: two at work while the third was being dressed. Two pairs were comm on in many mills, although both might not be in use at the same time.

The central eye of the runner stone has two cut grooves for engaging the rynd upon which the stone is hung. The rynd hangs on the mace at the top of the sndle, the whole of which is supported at the bottom by a bridge tree. The runner stone must wear evenly as it turns, and its fine balancing is one of the miller's skills. Tentering is the term for adjusting the clearance between the stones by using a tentering screw at the bottom of the spindle. The gap size depends on the grain type, the condition of the stones and the speed they are turning.

Traditionally, the miller or millwright dresses the stones with a bill held at right angles to peck the stone surface. The heavy runner stone has to be carefully lifted out using a crane, and turned over so its underside can be dressed. The whole operation, including

Two pairs of millstones are housed in wooden tuns on this iron hurst frame, at Cann Mills, near Shaftesbury. These stones, along with others in the mill are in daily use.

This flour sifter at Cann Mills was manufactured by Armfields of Ringwood.

Three millstones at Cann Mills. Left to right: Peak, French burr, and composition (sickle dressed).

maintenance of surrounding gearing, might occupy two days. In a busy mill this may have had to take place every fortnight or so.

Stones are mounted on a strong hurst frame, originally of wood and forming an integral part of the mill by supporting the stone floor. Hurst frames are also free-standing as in the case of later iron examples. The stones are contained within a round wooden vat or tun upon which is the horse supporting the hopper and shoe. A chute supplies grain to the hopper from the bins on the floor above. The damsel, fixed to the mace and turning with the stone, agitates the shoe to feed the grain evenly into the eye of the runner stone. The miller can control the rate by pulling the crook string to alter the angle of the shoe.

According to requirements, the ground meal may be sifted or sieved to remove some or all of the broken husks or bran. After the seventeenth century there were rotating machines, such as the bolter where fine flour was forced out through a rotating cloth sleeve. This was followed by the wire machine which could separate different grades of flour at one time. Reels were introduced from France in the mid-nineteenth century.

Different types of stone can be seen either whole or as broken fragments at mill sites. Millstones and querns from 'La Penne' were common in the twelfth to fifteenth centuries, most probably from Pen Pits, an extensive area of surface workings near Penselwood on the border with Somerset and Wiltshire. Old red sandstone conglomerate from the Quantocks or South Wales was either brought overland from Somerset or through the south coast ports. This stone was suitable for grinding animal feeds. The most common stones are of millstone grit from the Derbyshire Peak District. Known as 'peaks' or 'greys', these medium-coarse stones were better for grinding barley or animal feeds than for wheat. Dark basaltic lava stones known as 'blacks' or 'cullens' were imported from Mayen and Neidermendig in Germany, a source of stone exploited from the Roman period onward. The most prized millstones are still the French burr-stones, imported in great numbers after about 1800 from La Ferte-sous-Jouarre and Epernon in the Paris basin. This hard flint-like stone was not usually found in pieces large enough to make a single mill stone, so they were often made in 12 shaped segments backed with plaster and held together with iron hoops. There is a rare example of a four-piece burr-stone at

Additional equipment in a watermill includes machinery such as this simple corn cleaner with wire cylinder at White Mill.

A close-up of a French burr-stone, showing the typical construction in segments, held in place by iron bands.

Mangerton Mill. Composite millstones are artificial 'stones' made with emery and cement. Although they were much cheaper than burrs and needed less dressing, their main use was for milling animal feeds.

The traditional method of milling with stones received a severe blow from roller milling which was introduced into Britain in 1862 and rapidly gained a dominant hold in the industry. Larger quantities could be milled and the machinery was well adapted for powering by steam engines. Large steam roller mills at the ports became increasingly important for flour milling, providing the needs of the ing populations of larger towns and cities. With few exceptions, however, most of Dorset's rural mills continued to use stones.

COUNTRY MILLS

The importance of water power is illustrated by the concentration of mills along some of Dorset's lesser streams. For example, it was reported in 1823 that within a mile of the sea at Lyme Regis, the short River Lim (partly in Devon) had seven mills: for corn or grist (2), cloth manufacturing (3), oil and fulling. In the later nineteenth century, four corn mills were still operating within a similar distance along the Sturkell Brook, a tributary of the Stour in north Dorset. In the east, the River Allen had at least nine water-powered sites along its 12-mile course between Wimborne St Giles and Wimborne. These included corn mills, a bone mill, paper mill and saw mill. In and around Sydling St Nicholas there were six waterwheels (mostly on farms) within two miles of the source of Sydling Water, with two more mills before this five-mile tributary joined the River Frome at Grimstone. In the neighbouring valley, the longer River Cerne had eight mills in four miles at Cerne Abbas, Nether Cerne, Godmanstone and Forston. A

Shillingstone Bere Marsh Mill, c.1885, with miller Frederick Rickman.
This rural mill closed in 1923 and has been demolished.

Netherbury Mill and mill house alongside, now a private residence.

south tributary of the Frome flows between heaths at Empool Bottom, where Warmwell Mill stands derelict among extensive watercress beds.

As well as its tributaries, the River Frome also served corn mills and farm wheels, but there were always problems in these valleys where watermeadow systems and mill wheels were both competing for water. Maiden Newton has the most impressive mill, in brick and stone with a large 16ft diameter by 10ft wide waterwheel by Winter & Hossey of

Dorchester on the west wall. Part of the mill is now occupied by an engineering works. Many mills along the Frome have been converted to houses, such as Water Barn at East Burton where an undershot wheel is visible from a footpath. Two other streams draining into Poole Harbour have mill buildings surviving: North Mill and West Mill (both now houses) on the Piddle or Trent at Wareham, and Morden Mill (with a turbine) on Sherford Water between Bere Regis and Lytchett Minster.

Scattered deep in the countryside away from the main rivers, there were more corn mills powered by numerous smaller streams. To the south west of Sherborne, for example, there were mills on the north-flowing tributaries of the River Yeo at Chetnole, Holt (Melbury Osmond) and Halstock, all now converted to houses. In west Dorset, there were mills on the River Brit and its tributaries around Beaminster, Netherbury and Stoke Abbott, several being flax mills. Netherbury Mill, with a turbine, is still an impressive building with a bell high up on the west gable and a mill house alongside.

Mills with waterwheels on the River Asker include Hembury Mill (Askerswell) and Old Mill (Loders), a house but retaining its undershot wheel beside a lane. The tributary Mangerton River has Mangerton Mill in working order, while upstream Powerstock Mill (West Milton) is now a house with the external wheel and leat course surviving. Near Broadoak in the Marshwood Vale, the tiny River Char powered a 15ft diameter wheel at Stoke Mill which was occupied from just before 1860 by Samuel Moores. Flour was used in a bake house opposite to produce bread and the famous Dorset knob biscuits. Moores moved to the present bakery at Morcombelake in 1879. The higher reaches of the Axe had a string of mills at Mosterton, of which Buckham Mill stands in a typical rural scene with its pond and farmhouse.

The Stour River is by far the most rewarding river to explore for mills. The first site in Dorset is the Maggs and Hindley flax and iron works at Bourton (now a food factory) which had at least three waterwheels, including one of 60ft diameter. Downstream, Waterloo Mill at Silton and Eccliffe Mill below Gillingham are now houses, then there is a small mill at High Bridge Farm, East Stour, where a turbine is now silted-up alongside the waterwheel pit. Stour Provost Mill, with

High Bridge Mill, East Stour. This small mill on the Stour was worked by a wheel before a turbine was later installed alongside.

a wheel by E.S. Hindley of Bourton, 1889, was restored in the 1980s to generate electricity. There was a Domesday mill here and at least one corn mill and a fulling mill were recorded in the sixteenth and seventeeth centuries. Mills at Marnhull and Fifehead have been demolished, but West Mill near Stalbridge has a disused Hindley wheel (1893) and is partly occupied by an animal feed producer.

King's Mill, a stone building under a slate roof dating from the late 1820s, stands by the Stour just above King's Mill Bridge near Marnhull and last worked in 1935. Its interior was restored in 1993, but the undershot wheel remains derelict and the weir needs rebuilding if this mill is to work again. Cut Mill is at a picturesque spot next to a small bridge and a large weir down in the valley below Hinton St Mary. Stone and brickwork show the small mill to have been enlarged and rebuilt two or three times. Armfield of Ringwood provided hatches and mill machinery inside in 1910. The internal undershot wheel is dilapidated.

Sturminster Newton Mill is one of the best known mills in Dorset and is open to the public. Fiddleford Mill is the next downstream, just

Cut Mill and weir on the River Stour, Hinton St Mary, where the use of both brick and stone shows how the mill has been extended.

below a weir and footbridge and close to the late fourteenth century Fiddleford Manor (English Heritage). It is a small mill with an interesting stone inscription attributed to miller Thomas White; its date of 1566 probably records the occasion when an earlier timber mill was rebuilt in stone. Now disused, Fiddleford Mill contains an Armfield turbine. Mills at Shillingstone and Durweston have been demolished. Below Blandford Forum, a footpath passes Keynston Mill, containing a derelict undershot wheel, before crossing the valley floor to Spetisbury, where an undershot wheel pit marks the site of a mill on another course of the Stour. Next downstream is White Mill, restored and open to the public.

After Wimborne, Canford Mill was destroyed in a fire in 1894, but at Holdenhurst can be seen the large Throop Mill, rebuilt in 1912 when an upper floor was added and a 60-inch Armfield turbine installed. From this pulleys and belts drove four roller mills as well as grain cleaners, flour dressers, augers and elevators. Parsons & Sons

Throop Mill and weir across the Stour, in 1948: the last large corn mill before the Stour reaches the sea. It ceased work in 1972.

bought the mill in 1926, supplying their bakery business with flour. Messrs Heygates of Northampton took over in 1957 but milling stopped in 1972 when the supply of water was diminished as a result of a flood-relief scheme. Cecil Biles was the last miller from 1929 until closure. A mill on this site was owned by Quarr Abbey (Isle of Wight) before being granted to Christchurch Priory at the end of the thirteenth century. Some flour was made into ships' biscuits nearby in the nineteenth century. Finally, Place Mill at Christchurch is also open to the public.

TOWN MILLS

Towns such as Bridport, Dorchester, Gillingham, Lyme Regis, Wareham and Wimborne Minster all had at least one mill in their environs; surprisingly, there was no mill at Blandford Forum. There were village mills too, with survivals, for example, at Corfe Castle, Litton Cheney, Charminster, Godmanstone and Sutton Poyntz. Milling became more important to towns as their populations increased in the nineteenth century. Some of the older traditional mills continued at work, such as the recently restored Town Mill at Lyme Regis, which is described on page oo.

There are two notable later Victorian mill buildings, at Bridport and Dorchester. At the former, West Mill is an impressive brick-built mill alongside West Street, dating from 1878-80 when the old mill was totally rebuilt in an east-west alignment. The old waterwheel was removed and the three pairs of millstones were instead driven by a turbine manufactured by Hick Hargreaves & Co. of Bolton. John Fowler was miller from at least 1895 until 1939. He and his family were also millers in this period at East Mill on the River Asker. Having lain fire-damaged for fifteen years, West Mill was repaired and became an architect's office in 1989. Some of the machinery, including the turbine, a Canadian winnowing machine and grain elevators, was retained inside the mill. Although still preserved, the millstones are no longer in position on the stone floor. Outside, the lucam can be seen high up on the west gable wall. The water intake for the turbine and overflow pass beneath the building.

Prior to its rebuilding West Mill was occupied in 1864-75 by Henry Hansford, who leased it from the Gundrys for an annual rent of £101. Earlier in the nineteenth century the mill is said to have been run by Thomas Legg as a grist and bolling mill. A 1770s plan of Bridport published in John Hutchin's *History of Dorset* shows West Mill at right angles to the street and straddling a leat from the River Brit.

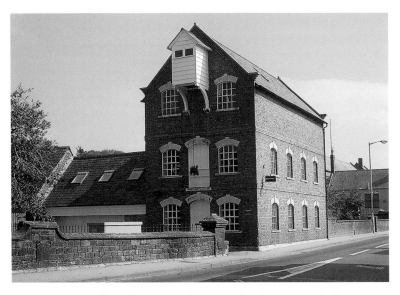

West Mill, Bridport, is a fine example of a purpose-built mill of the later nineteenth century. Note the lucam housing the sack hoist on the end wall.

Three other corn mills at Bridport, but on the River Asker, were East Mill, Folly Mill and South Mill, which served Bothenhampton.

Fordington Mill, Dorchester, provides a good example of a large town mill fitted out with the very latest milling equipment in the late Victorian period. The site was listed in Domesday Book and by 1211 King John had granted it to Bindon Abbey. In 1349, a fulling mill was added. The mill was rebuilt in 1590 and 1607 by William and John Churchill. By the 1840s it had been rebuilt as two corn mills. In 1891-2 it was transformed into a steam roller mill by J. Watkins of Dorchester for Arthur J. Legg, 'a large farmer and a well-known sheep-breeder.' Legg had owned the mill for some years, but had come to a point where he was compelled to work it or close it. He ventured to build a substantial new mill containing the latest type of plant, which he ordered from Thomas Robinson & Son Ltd of Rochdale.

Legg spared no expense in procuring machinery, from cleaning machines to roller mills, with a magnetic separator, to make his mill 'one of the most perfect in the country.' *The Dorset County Chronicle*

An old view showing Fordington steam flour mill at work. Note the chimney for the steam engine and the tailrace (bottom, centre), for part of the mill was still water-powered.

used glowing terms to report the new mill's official opening in 1892 and gave a good account of the working of a roller mill of the time. The steam power came from a 100HP compound tandem condensing engine with a Lancashire boiler, manufactured by Robinsons. At the opening ceremony, Miss May Brown named the engine 'May', the high pressure cylinder 'Pioneer' and the low pressure cylinder 'Industry'.

From the street outside two conveyors elevated the wheat to the grain silos, which could hold about 375 cwt. From here the wheat was blended and cleaned - 'a very complicated and elaborate automatic process . . . the necessary machinery being a marvel of ingenuity.' To thoroughly clean the wheat and remove impurities, the grain passed through warehouse separators and rotary sieves, barley and cockle cylinders to remove the non-wheat and small seeds, followed by quick revolving scourers and brushes so the wheat reached the roller mill 'in an thoroughly fit state.'

The roller mill was on four floors, including a basement. The first floor had six double roller mills, two for breaking the wheat down and cleaning the bran, and four for flouring the middlings. There was also a magnetic separator for taking out nails and other metallic substances. On the floor above were four 'Koh-i-noor' purifiers, a rotary scalper and two separating sieve purifiers. The third floor had flour dressing machines, two double rotary scalpers and and a separating sieve purifier. On the top floor were the elevator heads and spouting for conveying the produce to the different machines, and the sack hoist. Meanwhile, the older section of the mill was used as a provender mill, with three sets of stones driven by a 24-inch 'Little Giant' turbine installed 'a few years ago.' This had a 9ft head and gave excellent results with no need for repair.

'For a nominal three sacks per hour plant it will be seen that Mr Legg has an unusually complete outfit, and when we add that he contemplates adding a conditioning plant, and that the electric light is being installed by Mr Newman of Taunton, it is clear that Mr Legg intends to be in the front van of milling progress and reform. He is

Fordington Mill is only just recognisable today, converted into flats.

now turning out an excellent flour, more granular, perhaps, than that to which the neighbourhood has been accustomed; but the virtues of granular flour will soon make themselves apparent to the bakers.'

The Dorset County Chronicle ended its account on an optimistic note not borne out by reality. 'Situated in the midst of a good English wheat district, Mr Legg has, like many other millers of energy, shown that the small country mill is not doomed to die out under pressure from its big neighbours in the ports.' Home-grown wheats were carted to Dorchester for milling, while imported wheats were brought by rail from Bristol and London. By 1923 the mill was worked by the Dorchester Roller Flour Mills Co. Ltd.

Subsequently, Fordington Mill closed and was much altered in appearance by the Mill Street Housing Society in 1940 and 1986. There remains some trace of its former function, such as a preserved stone carved with a figure, the initials WC and date 1590, referring to William Churchill. No longer visible, the carving also included the motto 'Do well to all men' which was taken as the trademark for Legg's new steam mill. A stone carved 'AIL 1891' high on the east gable of the main four-storey mill is a record of Arthur Legg.

INDUSTRIAL MILLS

While corn milling was the commonest user of water power, other applications were of some significance. Fulling mills, also known in the West Country as 'tucking mills', appeared by the beginning of the thirteenth century for the treatment of woollen textiles. Woven cloth was shrunk or felted and cleaned by being placed in a vat with a mixture of Fuller's earth and urine where it was pounded by wooden fulling stocks operated by a water wheel. These were like large hammers which were lifted by cams on the turning waterwheel before dropping onto the cloth. This early water-powered industrial process was a spin-off from the once important West Country woollen textile industry and declined by the eighteenth century.

Fulling mills were often sited alongside exisiting corn mills, or even in the same building. The earliest reference to a fulling mill in Dorset is said to have been at East and West Stour in 1300. By 1408-9, a fulling mill had been built at Hogford Mill, on the River Allen at Pamphill near Wimborne, where a corn mill already existed. The Kingston Lacy Estate accounts for 1427 refer to materials for repairing the mill, including 12d on wages for carting clay (Fuller's earth?) to the mill. This fulling mill was relatively short-lived, for it is not recorded in the sixteenth century. It is likely that business was taken over by Walford Mill downstream, which is recorded as a fulling mill in 1552 and 1591. The site of Hogford Mill is today under pasture but traces survive of earthworks of buildings, ponds and water courses.

In 1569-70 there was a fulling mill and corn mill at Stour Provost, and in 1651 there were two corn mills, perhaps in the same building, and a fulling mill. The name 'Racky Close' for two fields on the 1840 Tithe Map would appear to refer to the tentering racks for stretching, drying and bleaching the fulled cloth. A seventeenth century estate map of Bindon near Wool has drawings depicting a 'Tucken' mill with

Louds Mill, near Dorchester. Little now survives of this
once substantial fulling and cloth mill.

an external waterwheel and hatches across the stream, and a nearby
grist mill with an internal wheel. Louds Mill, downstream from
Dorchester, was built in the 1590s for fulling and an early seventeenth
century map shows tentering racks nearby. It was later a cloth mill,
and Pigot's *Directory* of 1830 records William Stanton here as a
'woollen cloth manufacturer'. Today only part of the east wall of the
substantial mill survives, incorporated in a warehouse of Bredy
Agricentre.

There were other examples of fulling mills at Bridport, Cerne
Abbas, Lyme Regis and Wareham (Carey Farm). Place Mill and Knapp
Mill at Christchurch were both used for fulling for a time before
reverting to corn milling.

Water power was applied to silk throwing (spinning) at Sherborne
and Gillingham. At Westbury, Sherborne, a corn mill on the River Yeo
was taken over in 1753 by John Sharrer from Spitalfields for throwing
raw silk imported from Italy and the Far East. The silk was woven in
London. Upon his death in 1769, Sharrer's nephew William Willmott
took over the business which remained in the family for many years.
The industry is said to have employed some 600 workers at its height.
There were other silk mills in the town. For example, Pigot's *Directory*

Gillingham silk mill (left) and town mill, from a painting by David Gentleman (of about 1970). The whole site has since been redeveloped and this scene is now unrecognisable.

lists two silk throwsters: Thomas Willmott at Westbury, and John Gouger at Abbey Mills. Weaving took over when the Willmotts finished spinning at Sherborne in 1887. Fifty years later, Frederick Marsden of Coventry bought the mill for weaving rayon. Work in the Second World War included weaving silk parachutes, but in 1942 Marsden introduced fibre glass weaving for electrical insulation. CS Interglas Ltd. now occupy the site.

In Gillingham, the Gillingham Silk Co. was established by Stephen Hannam and others in 1769 next to his corn mill on Shreen Water, a tributary of the Stour. The silk mill employed about 160 people, many of them girls apprenticed from London workhouses 'to learn the art and mystery of a silk throwster.' In 1830, Pigot's *Directory* lists Samuel Hannam 'miller and silk throwster' here. When water levels were low, the silk mill (being the major employer) had priority over the corn mill. The silk mill closed in 1895 but the Town Mill continued, changing from corn milling to other uses until eventually

Clenham Flax Mill near Netherbury, in 1890. The use of waterpower to process locally grown flax was once common in West Dorset.

the whole site was demolished in 1988 after a serious fire. Other water-powered silk mills were worked higher up Shreen Water in Wiltshire, at Hincke's Mill and Lordsmill near Mere. Smaller silk mills were recorded in Dorset at Cerne and Court's Mill, Marnhull.

In north Dorset, Oliver and Uriah Maggs had two flax mills at Bourton until the 1880s; both were originally water-powered. But in the west there were many more mills for peparing and spinning flax for sailcloth, for example on the River Brit at Beaminster, Slape Mill, and Pymore Mill. Horsehill Mill and Clenham Mill were flax mills on the tributary between Stoke Abbott and Netherbury. Mangerton Mill was partly a flax mill, while Grove Mill on the River Bride at Burton Bradstock retains an inscription: 'This flax-swingling mill, the first introduced into the West of England, was erected by Richard Roberts, 1803.' The mill later became Rendall's flour mill (turbine) and bakery.

Connected to the rope and twine making industry of Bridport were bolling mills which used tilt hammers to crush flax and hemp stems and to separate the fibres. Before it was rebuilt, part of Bridport's West Mill had been a bolling mill for a while. Further down the River Brit, Port Mill was another bolling mill. By the 1880s this had become a grist mill to provide feed for the dray horses at the nearby Old Brewery. Folly Mill, Bridport, was converted to steam in the 1880s and used as a grist mill and net making machine works. It had an iron breastshot wheel of 12ft diameter which was being used for electricity generation in about 1950.

Paper mills required not just water power but also clean water, which many of Dorset's chalk streams could supply. Although the actual paper making continued by hand until suitable machinery was invented, water power was first needed for pulping and beating the fibres of the raw materials which included flax, grown in west Dorset, and old rags, sailcloth and rope which were available from ports such as Bridport and Poole.

There was a paper mill at Beaminster from the mid-eighteenth century until about 1814, but the two main locations were in the east, all within reach of Poole Harbour. These water-powered paper mills were mostly small and produced coarse wrapping papers. At Wareham, South Carey Mill (built in 1747) and West Mill worked until 1817 and 1831 respectively.

Wimborne was a more important centre, where the original paper mill was Buckets Mill (a corn mill), established by about 1700 and said to have been the earliest site in Dorset. There is a reference to George Rogers 'at ye paper-mills at Wimborne' in the Poole Town accounts of 1732, and a paper mill at Canford Bridge was first documented in 1739. The Poole Port Books record paper carried to London in 1704, most likely from Wimborne. Isaac Taylor's Dorset map of 1765 shows a paper mill off Poole Road, Wimborne. Increasing pollution in the River Allen led Stephen Burt to move upstream to Witchampton by 1780. Once a bone-crushing mill, this was to grow into a large paper making concern which continued almost to the end of the twentieth century. By 1851, woodpulp and esparto grass were among the raw materials and paper making machinery had been introduced, including a 77-inch Fourdrinier machine. Ten years later Burt was employing 62 workers. He was joined by his son, also William, and in 1889 a waterwheel was replaced by a 40-inch diameter turbine of 45.6HP. A private company was set up in 1924, specialising in wall papers, box papers, cover paper and boards. The paper mill closed in the 1980s.

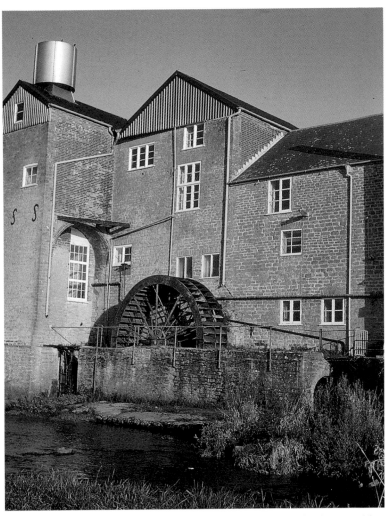

The 19ft waterwheel is a prominent feature at the rear of Palmer's Old
Brewery, Bridport. This iron wheel was manufactured in 1879
by T. Helyear of Bridport.

At least three Dorset breweries made use of waterpower. The finest
example is at Bridport, where J.C. & R.H. Palmer's Old Brewery has
a low breastshot waterwheel, 19ft diameter by 5ft wide, made of iron
by T. Helyear of Bridport in 1879. A spur wheel on the wheel shaft

drove, via shafts, pulleys and belts, two pumps for drawing water from the brewery's well. The wheel can be seen from a road bridge across the River Brit behind the brewery. Hall & Woodhouse's original brewery at Ansty had a small iron waterwheel which powered machinery via a long shaft. The stream here is small and an earth dam formed a mill pond. Newman & Sons' village brewery at Sydling St Nicholas harnessed the Sydling Brook by a chain drive taken from a small iron undershot wheel 10ft diameter and 1ft 9in wide. Having remained idle since 1905 when the brewery was bought and closed by brewers John Groves of Weymouth, this wheel was scrapped in 1966 and the building converted to a house.

Saw mills were also water powered. There were twin mills at Mangerton and Puddletown, each with a corn mill and a saw mill. Mangerton, originally a flax mill, had its earlier waterwheel replaced by a turbine to operate circular, band and horizontal saws. In 1885, Joshua Allen was operating circular and band saws at the Friary Mill at Dorchester, where corn grinding, cracking and bruising was also undertaken. Allen advertised 'a good stock of felloes, stocks, ash, beech, and oak plank, elm and fir board always on hand.' At Wimborne an undershot wheel, 10ft 6in diameter by 12ft wide, worked a saw mill from the River Allen close to Poole Road. There had been a paper mill here until about 1830 and the wheel may have been first installed by the papermakers. By 1851, wood turning and rake making was taking place and in 1867 a sawmill was recorded. In 1880, Jos. Phillips & Sons moved into the land opposite, setting up a steam saw and turning mills. The waterwheel worked until about 1930. Its remains survive.

There were two water-powered mills for crushing bones on the River Allen, at Witchampton and upstream at Bidecombe Mill, near Gussage All Saints. Oil mills, for crushing linseed from the local flax, were recorded in the early nineteenth century at Lyme Regis and Wynford Eagle, and a snuff mill at Chetnole worked until the mid-nineteenth century.

In the twentieth century, many mills were converted to generate electricity for local use.

FARM WHEELS

Farms and estates used water power where it was available to work millstones, animal feed machinery, milking machines, sawmills and water pumps.

Three farm wheels can be viewed from public ways. A prominent example is at Roke Farm, beside a lane between Bere Regis and Milborne St Andrew, where an undershot or very low breastshot wheel, 15ft diameter by 4ft wide, is in the little Bere Stream next to a farm building with a date stone 'SEED 1890'. It used a ring drive (by Lott & Walne) to work animal feed crushers in the barn until 1947 and was restored in 1983-85. The wheel is notable for being close to the stream's spring, but a long narrow mill pond on the other side of the lane conserved water until required. There are three millstones set in a nearby wall.

Forston Farm in the Cerne valley has a low breastshot wheel, 16ft diameter by 5ft 5in wide, which can be seen from the A352 and a bridleway one mile south of Godmanstone. The iron wheel was made by Hossey of Dorchester and a ring drive by Lott & Walne of

The Roke Farm wheel, showing the hatch and ring drive gearing.

The Forston Farm wheel, with ring drive, survives in a well-built wheelpit beside the River Cerne.

Dorchester bolted to the rim engaged a pinion with a long shaft to work a pump, saw, millstones and crusher in a nearby barn. It last worked a milking machine before being replaced by a diesel engine because of increasingly unreliable water supplies. The short leat from the Cerne, where there are three hatches, is exceptionally well built in brick. The tailrace passes away under a water meadow stream.

A footpath passes another waterwheel at Blashenwell Farm near Corfe Castle. The millpond and spring source of water are immediately to the south. The iron breastshot wheel is 16ft diameter by 4ft 6in wide and has J-shaped and ventilated buckets. It was made

This iron waterwheel by Munden & Armfield of Ringwood survives beside a barn at Blashenwell Farm near Corfe Castle.

Detail showing the ring drive, pinion and lay shaft of the waterwheel at Trigon Farm, near Wareham. The lay shaft drove machinery in a farm building 300 feet away.

by Munden, Armfield & Co. of Ringwood in the second half of the nineteenth century and has a ring drive bolted to the arms at about 12ft diameter. The wheel, which last worked in 1943, is in a wheelpit in the farmyard next to a barn dated 1790.

A large overshot iron wheel, 26ft diameter by 2ft 2in wide, survives mainly below floor level in a barn at Toller Fratrum Farm. Made by Sprake of Bridport in 1832, its 16 round iron arms are held by half clamps and screwed at each end for tensioning, an unusual feature. A ring drive bolted to the arms at about half-diameter drove a pinion and shaft to work millstones, a chaff cutter and other machinery in the barn. Before the wheel ceased work in the 1940s, one of its last uses was to power sheep shears. Toller Fratrum, located on a small shelf above the Hooke Valley, is an unlikely site for Dorset's second largest waterwheel, but water was brought from a source over half a mile away by a leat, now filled in. Being hidden inside a farm building, the only clues outside are a dried up millpond at the back and a narrow iron aqueduct supported on a buttress and two pillars across a sunken lane.

Another farm wheel set below floor level is at Stalbridge Park, where the large Old Barn has a smaller stone extension with a slate roof on the south side. Within is an overshot wheel, 13ft 10in diameter by 3ft 2in wide, made by Maggs & Hindley in 1862. It worked a pair of millstones for preparing animal feeds and a countershaft and pulley drove a chaff cutter and turnip cutter. The watercourse is now dry but when available, there was said to be water to work the wheel for only 1fi hours.

There is an impressive 20ft diameter by 4ft wide pitchback wheel at Hewish Farm, one mile south of Milton Abbas. This iron wheel was made by Hossey of Dorchester, with a ring drive by Lott & Walne to drive a pump and threshing machine in a barn via a pinion and a 175ft underground shaft. It later drove an electricity generator. Another wheel by Hossey with a Lott & Walne ring drive is a 14ft diameter by 6ft wide high breastshot wheel at Trigon Farm near Wareham. A 300ft shaft through a tunnel to a farm building drove a generator of about 1901, as well as a circular saw bench and a pump. A governor near the generator controlled the wheel's speed by raising or lowering the hatch via a second shaft. The waterwheel stands by an unusual weir where complicated systems for managing water meadows include at least five hatches. The tail race from the wheelpit flows away under the river to meet another stream.

At least two estate saw mills used water power. There was an undershot wheel 14ft diameter by 6ft 8in wide at Charborough Park, while a saw mill at Bryanston Home Farm, near Blandford, was powered by a Gilkes turbine.

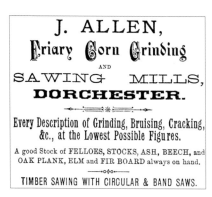

J. ALLEN,
Priary Corn Grinding
AND
SAWING MILLS,
DORCHESTER.

Every Description of Grinding, Bruising, Cracking, &c., at the Lowest Possible Figures.

A good Stock of FELLOES, STOCKS, ASH, BEECH, and OAK PLANK, ELM and FIR BOARD always on hand.

TIMBER SAWING WITH CIRCULAR & BAND SAWS.

WINDMILLS

Some 35 known or probable windmill sites in Dorset, with possibly six more, have now been identified, suggesting that windmills were more numerous in the county than previously thought. Most information comes from historic sources such as manorial records, tithe apportionment maps, other maps and place-name evidence. All the traditional windmills were for corn milling, and were built to catch the wind on high ground or near the coast. In the field today can be seen just a handful of possible windmill mounds, but there are two fine stone towers on Portland and a replica Portuguese windmill at Cann Mills in north Dorset. Just a few 'wind engines' were erected in the late nineteenth and early twentieth century for water pumping on farms.

The earliest windmills were of the post-mill type, built of timber around a strong central post supported by quarter bars and cross trees. The mill itself would have been weatherboarded and perhaps thatched, and a tail pole was used to turn it around the central post. The cross trees were anchored in a windmill mound and the cruciform foundation trench may survive. These mounds are difficult to date and they can be mistaken for Bronze Age barrows. Conversely, some genuine barrows were used for windmill mounds.

Tower mills became common in England by the early seventeenth century. These had a fixed stone tower with a cap containing the sails and windshaft which could be turned into the wind. The whole structure was also more solid than the post-mill. The sails were fitted on four stocks attached to the end of the windshaft which was held inside the cap and had a large brake wheel which was the equivalent of the pit wheel in a watermill. This engaged with a wallower and the power was transmitted downwards to a great spur wheel driving stone nuts and the millstones from above, a method called overdrift working.

Although they had been known in England since the mid-twelfth century, the first record of a windmill in Dorset was at Buckhorn Weston in 1267, beaten by neighbouring Somerset (1212 at Seavington St Michael), and Wiltshire (Ebbesbourne Wake, 1248). This is the first known reference to a windmill in an historical document - it is mentioned as part of a lady's dowry - and so it was possibly built a little earlier. Buckhorn Weston was well sited for a windmill, up on the Corallian ridge looking westward over part of the Blackmore Vale. Later references to windmills have been recorded at Chaldon Herring (1288), Pentridge (1293), Coombe Hayes (1310) and Wyke Regis (1314), this last being recorded as being worth 20s a year. There was a decline after the mid-fourteenth century (the Black Death no doubt helped) and it was not until the sixteenth century that new windmills appear again.

Small carvings at Milton Abbey Church and Abbot's Hall depict a windmill on a barrel or tun, which is the rebus (emblem) of Abbot William Middleton who undertook major building works around 1500. Such carvings are not necessarily accurate portrayals but nevertheless are of interest. There could be a connection with the known windmill site at Milton Abbas, shown later on Isaac Taylor's map of Dorset, 1765. Only three miles outside Dorset, it is worth visiting North Cadbury church in Somerset, where a superb bench end of 1538 shows a post mill, with a millstone lying on the ground for good measure.

A map of the Royal Forest of Gillingham, dated 1624, shows a windmill standing in a field named Little Down on the hilltop north of Shaftesbury. The Tithe Apportionment of 1845 has a 'Windmill Close' field, and a modern road in a housing estate retains the name. John Ogilby's road maps of 1675 often mark prominent landmarks such as windmills, so that his Bristol to Weymouth road map shows one at Melcombe Regis on the approach to Weymouth, and his Oxford to Poole road map shows another just outside Poole, although its location is rather unclear. Isaac Taylor's map of 1765 marks 'Windmill Point' at Baiter Point, which would seem to be the site of a windmill erected after 1543, when the townsfolk of Poole petitioned Henry VIII for them 'to erect make frame and set upp at in and upon your waste ground and Comon within the saide Towne called Baiter .

The Baiter Point post-mill and the town of Poole, from
an eighteenth century drawing.

. . one good and sufficient windmill to serve the saide Towne and
port.' A post mill is shown in a sketch 'A Prospect of the Town of
Poole from the West End of Bruncksey Island' published in John
Hutchin's classic *History and Antiquities of the County of Dorset*.
Taylor also marks 'windmill' just east of Milton Abbey on what is now
called Hoggen Down. The first edition Ordnance Survey 1-inch map
of 1811 marks 'Cashmore Mill' with a windmill symbol at Gussage St
Michael on Cranborne Chase. Thirty years later, the Tithe
Apportionment describes 'Windmill Field' here as arable.

Four windmill sites survive as names on modern Ordnance Survey
1:25000 scale maps. In north Dorset, 'Windmill Hill' (ST 729107) is
shown near King's Stag on the Holwell-Lydlinch border in the
Blackmore Vale. It is not on the Tithe Map. Just north of Sandford
Orcas village, 'Windmill Hill' (ST 623216) is well positioned half-way
up a west-facing escarpment overlooking Somerset. 'Windmill
Barrow' (SY 937977) at Windmill Barrow Farm, Lytchett Matravers,
may have been a windmill mound, 11ft high, pear-shaped, and about
100ft in diameter, and embanked with a circular depression in the top.
It stands on a ridge just east of Charlborough Tower and is now tree-
covered.

A low hill called 'Windmill Knap' (SZ 006801) just north of
Langton Matravers would appear to be the site of 'Old Windmill'
shown on Taylor's map of 1765. The site is in a good position to catch
winds blowing through the vale between the Purbeck chalk and

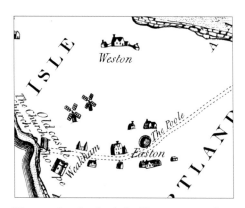

The two Portland windmills on a map of 1710.

limestone ridges. In the same area, there is a 68ft diameter windmill mound on Coombe Hill (SZ 009789), a small west-east ridge at Langton Matravers. A circular embanked hollow at Steeple (SY 909809), of about 12ft in diameter, is another possible windmill mound, with an entrance from a trackway in the corner of a settlement site.

While windmills were for corn milling, there were some wind-powered water pumps from the late nineteenth century onwards. In parts of Dorset, small wind engines were used to pump water for farm use. Most if not all of these are no longer in use. A six-vaned windmill was used for pumping water to reclaim St Andrew's Bay on Brownsea Island in Poole Harbour in the second half of the nineteenth century.

PORTLAND WINDMILLS

The earliest record of a windmill on Portland comes from Land Revenue Accounts in 1608. Two windmills are shown on William Simplon's map of 1626 and on an unusual map of 1710 published later in John Hutchin's *History of Dorset*, showing Portland on its side and with the two mills neatly drawn, each with four square sails. Isaac Taylor's map of Dorset, 1765, also marks them as drawings. These mills were ideally sited high on the Portland plateau, milling the corn grown in the open fields before quarrying scarred the island. They were also very necessary as Portland is virtually devoid of streams.

Portland's two derelict windmill towers in 1977. At this date
the north tower (foreground) still retained a sail stock and
its windshaft; these are now at the Portland Museum.

There was a local saying that if the wind was too gentle to turn both
mills, one would be stopped! In 1855, A. and E. Pearce were recorded
as wind millers on Portland. In 1885, Edward Pearce had one mill and
shared the other with Robert Pearce. Ten years later, Edward and
Robert Pearce were recorded as millers but the last windmill ceased
working at about this time.

It is surprising that the only two historic windmill towers surviving
in Dorset should be standing within a stone's throw of each other on
Portland. The two masonry towers at Easton are believed to date from
the seventeenth century. Both are about 23ft high and 12ft internal
diameter. The north mill (SY 691714) has vertical straight-sided stone
walls with dressed stone for a kerb around the top and the window
openings. This was the last mill to work in the 1890s, and for many
years the windshaft and a sail stock remained until removed for
preservation at the Portland Museum. This is an early example of a
windshaft, which had the sail stocks mortised through the timber. The
south mill (SY 692713) tapers towards the top, which may be the
result of rebuilding at some time in the past. Interestingly, the lower
part was adapted as a pill-box during the Second World War. The
tower stands between a deep quarry working and a quarry road.

HORSE MILLS

Horse mills were used for a variety of purposes, mostly on farms. The horse, donkey or mule walked in a circle attached to an arm which worked the mill or machinery, such as edge runner stones turning in a circular trough for crushing cider apples. In the mid-eighteenth century there was a mustard mill worked by a blind horse at Castleton, Sherborne. There was a horse mill for grinding malt by two rollers at Higher Melcombe at the end of the nineteenth century, the product being supplied to farmers and their workers for brewing beer. Chalmington Home Farm near Cattistock had a horse-driven well-pump, and another horse pumping gear was at Bloxworth House, near Bere Regis.

A remarkable survival is a horse mill house at West Farm, just south of Winterborne Whitechurch. Perhaps dating from the eighteenth century, it housed horse gear for working farm machinery on the east

This thatched circular horse mill house can be seen just south of the village at Winterborne Whitechurch. Horse mills were an answer to the problem of poor water supply.

side. This distinct wheelhouse is round, in brick with a conical thatched roof. It has an internal diameter of about 34ft and a bearing for a lay shaft is the only clue to its industrial past. Horse mill houses were often attached to a barn but this one stands alone across a lane from the main farm buildings.

Although not a 'mill' in the true sense, another application of horse power at a fixed site was in the Purbeck stone quarries, where horses or donkeys were used for raising stone up inclines from the underground 'quarrs'. The horse-rounds with crab-stones for holding the capstan still survive in the district between Langton Matravers and Swanage.

A 20-inch double 'British Empire' turbine by
Joseph J. Armfield of Ringwood, c.1900.

TURBINES

Towards the end of the nineteenth century water turbines became an alternative source of power to waterwheels. They used the available water more efficiently, were easy to operate and proved relatively trouble-free. Joseph J. Armfield of Ringwood became an important supplier of turbines in the south of England, and in the period 1887-1923, his firm supplied at least 31 turbines to sites in Dorset, mostly for corn mills but also for foundries or iron works, pumping water, generating electricity or other uses. The Armfield 'British Empire' turbine was the most popular. It was normal to have a belt drive taken from the turbine's vertical shaft, as can be seen today at Sturminster Newton where a turbine of 1904 is still at work. That it is still in good working order is a tribute to Armfield's design.

A testimonial published in *The Miller* in 1896 by William Burt of the Witchampton Paper Mill is typical of many. It refers to the installation of a British Empire turbine to replace 'a very good breastshot waterwheel, and I find I have not only gained power but there is an advantage in being able to run without any trouble during floods . . . You fixed and started it in April 1889 and it has not cost me one shilling in repairs.' Canford Mill on the Stour had three 45-inch diameter British Empire turbines, converted to generate electricity after the mill was burnt down in 1894.

Turbines for pumping were tried at the Longham Waterworks established by the Bournemouth & District Water Co. in 1885 to tap water in a gravel bed aquifer. This was the site of Longham Mill on the River Stour, where a weir with a head of water was utilised by a Trent turbine. It proved troublesome because of the river's irregular flow and was replaced in 1888 by steam pumping plant. A turbine was tried again in 1920-24, with one installed by Armfields, but this too was unreliable. There was turbine pumping on a smaller scale at West Lulworth, where a good spring had supplied water for a corn mill

Turbine and gearing supplied by C. Cadle of Dublin in the old wheel pit at Purn's Mill, on Shreen Water at Gillingham.

from the thirteenth century. In 1893 an 8-inch Armfield British Empire turbine was installed to drive a pump for the Weld estate, before being replaced by oil engines in a new building.

Not all turbines in Dorset were made by Armfields. An American turbine was installed for the saw mill at Mangerton, Hick Hargreaves & Co. of Bolton made the turbine for West Mill, Bridport, while Purn's Mill had a turbine supplied by C. Cadle, engineers, Dublin. All survive although not at work. The Home Farm on the Bryanston estate near Blandford had a turbine made in 1883 by Gilkes & Co., the famous manufacturers of Kendal, for driving a pair of millstones, barn machinery and woodworking plant. The necessary water was first pumped by a waterwheel down at the River Stour up to the large capacity Cliff Reservoir on the hill above, giving it a head of 100ft as it fell through a pipe to the turbine.

MILLWRIGHTS AND WHEEL MAKERS

Dorchester-based Hossey and Winter & Hossey made farm waterwheels, for example at Forston Farm (Cerne), Hewish Farm (Milborne Stream), Trigon Farm (Piddle), and West Stafford Farm (Frome). An impressive breastshot wheel, 16ft diameter by 10ft wide by Winter & Hossey survives at the west end of Maiden Newton Mill. Lott & Walne of Dorchester are credited with some waterwheels but their main contribution was mill gearing, hatches and other apparatus. For example they added ring drives to the Hossey wheels at Forston, Hewish and Trigon and the appearance of their name on the casting may have led to confusion in the past. Henry George Martin, established in 1890 at Dorchester, made the two overshot wheels for Winterborne Steepleton Mill.

In Bridport, Thomas Helyear of West Street made the 19ft diameter waterwheel at the Old Brewery in 1879. Other waterwheel makers here were J. Sprake who made the overshot wheel at Toller Fratrum Farm, and Gerrard Samson & Co. who cast the wheel (since removed) for the Town Mill, Lyme Regis, in 1888.

Charles Coombs was a millwright in North Street, Beaminster, from at least 1823, and is said to have specialised in broad overshot and high breastshot wheels. Examples of his wheels are an overshot wheel 16ft diameter by 6ft wide, dated 1866, at Litton Cheney Mill and a similar-sized low breastshot wheel of 1877 at West Mill, Sherborne. Both are visible from a road. At Chetnole Mill, an internal high breastshot iron wheel (14ft 4in diameter by 5ft wide), has cast 'Coombs Beaminster 1848'.

The names Maggs and Hindley are closely associated with Bourton. Daniel Maggs established a foundry next to a flax mill by 1815, and the earliest surviving all-iron waterwheel with a date has cast 'D. Maggs. 1819'. Formerly at Nether Cerne Manor Farm, it is now at Castleton, Sherborne. By 1842, Oliver and George Maggs were at the foundry and in 1848-59 Oliver Maggs was described as ironfounder, engineer & agricultural implement maker (also grist mill and flax mills). Edmund Samuel Hindley joined in the 1860s, first trading as Maggs & Hindley and then taking over by 1867 when he was also described as a millwright. He was joined by his sons until the 1920s when the foundry closed. Interestingly, Armfields supplied two small turbines in 1920-21 to the foundry, but there had been a 60ft diameter wheel here until 1918, as well as two smaller wheels. Waterwheels made by Maggs include the 1819 wheel; by Maggs & Hindley at Old Barn, Stalbridge dated 1862; waterwheels by E.S. Hindley survive at Melbury Abbas Mill (overshot, 1875), Cann Mills (overshot, 1880s), West Mill, Stalbridge (1893), and at Stour Provost (1889). Outside Dorset, the waterwheel at Stourhead Gardens was made by Hindleys in 1912, and a 16ft diameter high breastshot wheel and water pump of 1902 from Maiden Bradley, Wiltshire, is now displayed at the Kew Bridge Steam Museum, London. As millwrights, E.S. Hindley & Sons were employed for many years maintaining and repairing the wheel and pumps at Castleton.

William Munden of Ringwood, Hampshire, made waterwheels, such as at Alderholt Mill, clearly named 'W. Munden, Maker, Ringwood'. Munden founded a millwrighting business in 1862, and was joined in 1875 by Joseph J. Armfield (1852-1938) and they traded as Munden, Armfield & Co., making the wheel at Blashenwell Farm and another at Radipole. Armfield soon took total control and began expanding the business manufacturing milling equipment, waterwheels, sluices and, after 1887, water turbines. Joseph Armfield was well known for his turbines from the 1880s, but his firm also fitted waterwheels and other milling machinery. Cut Mill on the River Stour is an example, where the main hatch for the undershot wheel is by Armfield, as are those on the river itself.

WATER PUMPING

The water pumping station at Castleton, Sherborne, contains Dorset's largest waterwheel, at 26ft diameter by 3ft 9in wide. This impressive high breastshot wheel has been restored by the Castleton Waterwheel Restoration Society and is open to the public on the second Sunday in every month during the summer.

In 1859 the Committee of the Sherborne Local Board of Health resolved to improve sanitation by pumping clean water from a borehole to a reservoir off Bristol Road above the town. Two turbines driving ram pumps were not a success, so in 1869 a new pumphouse was built, containing a high breastshot waterwheel with pumps supplied and installed by Stothert & Pitt of Bath. The wheel used a ring drive to power three ram pumps capable of lifting 7,200 gallons per hour against a head of 235ft. The wheel was fed from three sources, the main one being the Upper Oborne Stream, brought by a concrete lined channel on a bank into a launder to make the wheel a high breastshot. The Lower Oborne stream was used in emergencies, as a breastshot, and between the two levels, a third water supply came via a pipe from Sherborne Castle Lake.

After many years of successful service, the Sherborne Urban District Council contracted Edward White & Co. of Redditch to rebuild the wheel in 1898. E.S. Hindley & Sons of Bourton were employed on repairs in the early 1900s. In 1926 the exposed part of the wheel was enclosed in corrugated iron after a 'minor accident' when a man fell in while the wheel was turning. It was decided in 1959 that repairs to the wheel and 90-year-old pump set were too expensive and, coupled with water supply losses, electric pumps took over. Other pumping has taken place alongside the site. A Hindley steam engine worked from 1876, followed by gas, oil and diesel engines. The Castleton Waterwheel Restoration Society has saved the wheel and its wheelhouse from demolition and has installed a pump set, made by

Sparrows of Martock in 1883, to replace the original pumps which had been scrapped.

A number of small wheels were employed on estates for raising water. In the Frome valley, for example, there were 6ft diameter pumping wheels at Higher Chalmington near Cattistock and in the Frome valley at Frampton House, the latter set below ground level to operate two bucket pumps via a crank, connecting rod and beam. In the Piddle valley, Lott & Walne supplied Athelhampton House in 1903 with a 7ft diameter by 2ft wide wheel to work an inverted three-ram pump by chain drive. In the Bride valley, a 10ft diameter overshot wheel was installed at Bridehead, Little Bredy, by Stennor & Gunn of Tiverton as late as 1920 to drive a Goodwin pump for raising water over 300ft to two reservoirs.

The River Stour had two waterwheel pumps for estates near Blandford Forum. The smallest was a 5ft 6in diameter by 3ft 10in wide undershot wheel with pumps by Easton & Erith. It worked from 1871 to about 1940 for the Smith-Marriott estate, pumping water from beside Blandford Weir at Blandford St Mary to a reservoir about a mile away. The second system, for the Bryanston estate, was larger and more complex and its development was related to the building of Bryanston House in 1888-93. A wheel 12ft diameter by 8ft wide originally worked an Armfield pump from a ring drive. A second pump installed in 1890 could also be driven by an auxiliary steam engine, and in 1893 two more pumps by Wenham & Waters of Croydon were installed. Water from a leat and well was pumped up to Gallup Reservoir (for farms and Durweston and Stourpaine villages) and to Cliff Reservoir (for cottages, Home Farm, a private brewery and the main house). In 1912 the Wenham pumps were driven by a Crossley gas engine which could be started with the waterwheel. An electric pump took over in 1948 for a few years. The Cliff Reservoir had a capacity of a million gallons and one of its functions was to supply water to a turbine for driving machinery in a building at Home Farm.

WORKING COMMERCIAL MILLS

One mile south of Shaftesbury, N.R. Stoate & Sons operate Cann Mills, the last truly commercial water-powered corn mill in the county. Probably on a Domesday site, the mill was rebuilt in about 1880 when the miller was David Hunt. By 1923, the Miles family were millers, previously from French Mill downstream (now a private house). In 1939 R. Miles & Son were here, and S.E. Miles & Son were at Melbury Abbas Mill upstream. Norman Stoate came to Cann in 1947 but the mill was destroyed by a fire in 1954, caused when a diesel engine used for driving stones overheated. The iron wheel survived and the mill was rebuilt as a concrete building in 1955-56. Norman's son Michael is now the miller at Cann Mills. The Stoate family had begun milling at Watchet in Somerset in 1832. A new large mill was built at Temple Back, Bristol, in 1912, but closed some time after amalgamation with Spillers in 1933.

At Cann, the rectangular mill stands below the dam of the millpond

Cann Mills in 1999. Dorset's last commercial water-powered corn mill has an unusual Portuguese-style windmill on the roof, making it a source of curiosity for motorists on the nearby A350.

Michael Stoate, miller, inspecting organic flour at Cann Mills in 1999.

on the Sturkell stream. Conspicuous on the flat roof of the mill is a Portuguese-style windmill built in 1971 and capable of driving a small pair of stones and a stone for tool sharpening. When it worked, it had triangular cloth sails. Across the yard is the grain store from which grain is elevated to a cleaner in the main mill building. Propped against the wall of the store are three different mill stones: a Peak or Derbyshire stone, a French burr-stone and a composite stone, this last with sickle-dressing.

Inside the mill building, on the lower floor, is the iron overshot waterwheel, 10ft 6in diameter by 5ft 4in wide, made by Hindleys in about 1880. The pit wheel is not used but has a large pulley wheel which takes the main belt drive. This in turn drives via belting and pulleys two pairs of French burr-stones. There is a single pair of 3ft 6in diameter burr-stones on an iron hurst frame made by Taskers of Andover (brought here from a mill at Tring). The stones have a modern plastic tun which is far easier to keep clean than the traditional wooden type. A second pair of stones is on an iron hurst by Ruston & Proctor of Lincoln. Only one pair is run at a time. The waterwheel also drives elevators and a flour dresser. A double pair of 4ft diameter burr-stones on an iron hurst frame are electrically driven, again one at a time. A fifth pair of burr-stones is also worked by electric motor. Ground flour is elevated to the first floor for dressing, where there is a flour sifter manufactured by J.J. Armfield of Ringwood. The product then returns for bagging, as flour or bran.

N.R. Stoate & Sons sell stone-ground wholemeal flour (including organic) mostly to specialist independent bakers and health food shops in south-west England. The products include 100% wholemeal flour (ideal breadmaking flour from high protein English hard wheat), plain brown flour (80%), 100% extra strong wholemeal flour (made with a large proportion of high protein Canadian wheat and well suited to modern commercial breadmaking), self raising flour (100% wholemeal and 81% brown), maltstar flour (a granary type, with wheat flour blended with malted wheat flakes, rye flour and malt flour), rye flour (for sour doughs and rye breads), tomato and basil bread flour, and fine and coarse bran.

Within a few miles of Cann, in the Blackmore Vale, are two provender or animal feed mills still at work, although no longer using water power. Purn's Mill on the Shreen Water near Gillingham was the Parham Mill painted by Constable. It is still worked by G.B. Matthews & Co. Ltd., a long established firm who have been here since at least the 1870s (they also worked the Town Mill at Gillingham in the 1930s and Eccliffe Mill from the 1890s until at least 1939). Electric-powered roller mills crush maize, wheat and oats before mixing with molasses and vegetable fats to produce different animal feeds, although 80% is in the form of pellets for dairy cattle. Markets for these feeds extend to a radius of about 40 miles. There is a date of 1883 on the substantial four-storey stone mill building which has been

Purn's Mill, Gillingham. The remaining part of the building dated 1883 is still in use as an animal feed mill. This is the site of the 'Parnham', or 'Gillingham Mill' (1826), painted by John Constable (see the front cover).

much modified since. A large waterwheel was replaced by a turbine (by C. Cadle of Dublin) which still remains in the old wheelpit at the rear of the mill.

A second rare example of a mill site still being worked commercially for animal feeds is West Mill, on the River Stour near Stalbridge. C.C. Moore now occupy a larger modern premises next to the small original mill which has a Hindley wheel of 1893 but no stones or machinery. An interesting piece of twentieth century history

The Ruston & Hornsby oil engine installed in 1943 to supplement the
waterwheel at West Mill, Stalbridge, and still in working order.

is attached to this mill, because a 40 HP Ruston & Hornsby oil engine
was installed in 1943 at the expense of the Royal Navy when water
was reduced by a new cut made for the River Stour to alleviate
flooding danger at their Henstridge air station (in neighbouring
Somerset). This engine was still at work on a weekly basis in early
1999.

MILLS OPEN TO THE PUBLIC

ALDERHOLT MILL (SU 119143) stands almost in Hampshire where the county boundary is marked by the river which provides its power. It takes water from the Allen River, which becomes the Ashford Water immediately downstream of Alderholt Bridge before joining the Hampshire Avon at Fordingbridge. There are references dating back to at least the 1330s when 'Padner's Mill' was part of the manor of Cranborne. The brick-built mill last worked in 1942, but was restored in 1986. The original waterwheel was inside but the present wheel is outside the rear of the mill, a good example of an iron breastshot wheel, 11ft diameter by 7ft 10in wide, said to have been made in about 1850. 'W. Munden Maker Ringwood' is cast on the shrouds of the wheel. Of special interest is the depressing sluice which is lowered so that water ponds back in the leat until it overflows onto the wheel. A pair of French burr-stones is operated at weekends to demonstrate the mill t o the public and produce a small quantity of wholemeal flour, which is sold here and at some local shops. Part of the building

Alderholt Mill is on the Dorset border, near Fordingbridge.

Mangerton Mill, near Bridport, showing the corn mill (left) and part of the old flax and saw mill (right). The millpond is behind the building.

is an art gallery and teashop, while the adjoining miller's house is now bed and breakfast accommodation. Telephone: 01425 653130.

BOAR MILL (SY 961822) on Byle Brook at Corfe Castle is a recently restored National Trust mill, this one with a small Armfield turbine. It was worked from 1874 to 1920 by the Battrick family, who continued as bakers here until 1952. At present it is open by appointment only. Telephone: 01929 481294. Corfe's other mill, West Mill, is a ruin.

MANGERTON MILL (SY 490957) is a double mill, with a grist mill on the north side and a flax mill on the south. For a while both were bolling mills but a sale notice of 1835 states that one had reverted to corn milling. The last miller was Charles Henry Marsh, from 1925 until 1966 when he was grinding barley and bruising oats for animal feed. There is a 12ft diameter by 4ft wide iron waterwheel with an oak wheel shaft to drive three pairs of millstones. The wheel was a high breastshot but was taken out and reversed to make it an overshot when the millpond level was raised. The wheel alongside for the saw mill was later replaced by a turbine of American manufacture. The corn mill, which grinds grain occasionally, was restored in 1988-89 and is open to the public with a museum of rural bygones and a tea room. Telephone: 01308 485224.

Place Mill is an historic building on the quay at Christchurch.

PLACE MILL (SZ 160924) at Christchurch was in Hampshire until 1974. This small mill is notable for its curious water arrangements, whereby it stands close to the quay beside the lower Stour into which its tailrace feeds, but takes its water via a half-mile leat from the River Avon. At the time of Domesday it belonged to the Canons of Holy Trinity and was valued at 30 pence. Early stonework at the base and sixteenth and nineteenth century brickwork in the present structure are evidence that the mill has been rebuilt and altered many times. For a while it became a fulling mill before reverting to corn milling. After the Dissolution in 1539, it passed into royal hands and then through various owners until 1888 when the mill, miller's cottage, garden and mill leat were sold to Christchurch Borough Council. In 1878 Andrew

Cox, who had been with his father at Corfe Mullen Mill, became miller. Work ceased in 1908 when the mill became too expensive to maintain. Mr Cox moved away, returning in 1916 to Knapp Mill at Christchurch. For 70 years from 1910 Place Mill was leased out as a boat repair shop and store. Then in 1981 restorations were begun to re-open the mill as a craft centre while maintaining the 10ft 6in diameter undershot wheel and millstones in working condition so that milling could be demonstrated to the public.

STURMINSTER NEWTON MILL (ST 782135) is on a Domesday site. Lands around Sturminster were granted by King Edgar to Glastonbury Abbey in 968AD and a century later the Domesday Survey recorded that Glastonbury had three mills, worth 40 shillings. One of the sites was undoubtedly the present one just upstream from Sturminster's fine medieval bridge across the Stour, beside a weir where hatches control the water. It is a well chosen site, with a reliable water supply from the river all the year around. The mill seen today is L-shaped, with a stone-built section said to date from 1648 and a brick extension of the eighteenth century. There were two internal waterwheels, renewed in 1849 by William Munden, and then finally replaced in 1904 by one of Joseph Armfield's British Empire turbines, 45-inch diameter and rated at 22 HP. A sluice below water level can be operated from inside the

Sturminster Newton Mill. This view of 1899 shows
the miller's cottage, since demolished.

mill to regulate the turbine. The main vertical turbine shaft has a large flywheel with a belt to drive the French burr millstones, while two bevelled crown wheels with pinions and lay shafts operate crushers, a winnowing machine, sack hoists and a tall vertical mixer. Of interest in the brick wing are two hammer mills (each with 12 hammers) installed in about 1947 and driven from a lay shaft.

Milling continued at Sturminster until 1969, followed by a short period when animal feed was produced by a local farmer. After concern for the future, a Trust was established and the mill was repaired and restored to working order in 1981. Surminster Newton Mill is run by the Sturminster Newton Mill and Museum Society and is open to the public during summer months. Telephone: 01258 473760.

TOWN MILL, LYME REGIS (SY 342922) is believed to be on a Domesday site (worth 39 pence) and was the lowest of seven known water-powered sites along the last mile of the River Lim. Some of the stonework may date from 1340 when Edward III granted a Letter Patent to the town for the erection of a new mill, with a rental of 7s. The building seen today, however, has its origins in the 1640s (it had to be rebuilt after damage during the Civil War siege of Lyme in 1642). It was restored in the late nineteenth century, and worked as a corn mill until the late 1920s. There is evidence for two overshot waterwheels, one external and the other internal. The latter, an iron wheel made in 1888 by Samson of Bridport, was the last to work and was taken out in about 1940 when a turbine was installed to help with the electricity supply for Lyme Regis. The generator was on the top floor of the mill, but the turbine was never fully successful because of the small stream of water available. It supplemented a main diesel generator in the malthouse. By 1991 the site was derelict when it was taken over by the Town Mill Trust with the aim of restoring this great town asset to full working order. Three pairs of Peak millstones remained inside, with the sack hoist, spur wheel and pit wheel. A replacement waterwheel, a little smaller than the original, was acquired from Lower Torr, Kingston, in South Devon. This is an iron wheel, 12ft diameter by 4ft wide, made in 1878 by Bearne & Sons of Newton Abbot. In addition to restoration of the mill machinery, ancillary buildings have been renovated for a gallery, craft workshops and restaurant, making this an attractive amenity for the public at the end of Mill Lane, Lyme Regis. There survives a unique documentary record of the mill from the eighteenth century town account rolls. A report on the recent archaeological survey and excavation is to be published.

UPWEY MILL (SY 663851) is a fine stone-built mill of 1802 with four floors, seen alongside Church Street, Upwey. Its impressive waterwheel (22ft diameter by 9ft wide) is fed from two sides at different levels: a higher leat which turns the wheel as an overshot and a stream taken from the River Wey to turn it from the other side as a backshot. Although Upwey Mill is not at present open to the public, it is hoped to be restored and opened for its bicentenary year, 2002. Meanwhile, visits can be arranged by appointment only. Telephone: 01305 816016.

Upwey Mill near Weymouth dates from 1802 and has a large waterwheel powered by two different streams.

Walford Mill at Wimborne has found a new life as an arts centre.

WALFORD MILL (SU 009007) on the River Allen at Wimborne is a mostly nineteenth century brick building, on the site of an earlier mill. There is some evidence for two internal undershot wheels, and a tall chimney stack was for a steam engine supplying additional power. The Walford Mill Craft Centre has been here since 1986.

WHITE MILL (ST 958006) on the north bank of the Stour near Shapwick was probably listed in 'Domesday Book'. Originally part of a royal manor, the mill was sold in the sixteenth century, passing through three owners until being purchased in 1773 by Henry Bankes. The

White Mill, part of the Kingston Lacy estate, has been restored by the
National Trust and contains rare wooden mill gearing.

Joyce family were the millers at that time and remained here until
Thomas Joyce was the last miller in 1885. Traces of limestone and
heathstone walling may date to an earlier mill, but the mainly brick-
built mill under a tiled roof seen today dates from a rebuilding of 1776
(there is a dated keystone above the millrace) initiated by Bankes.
There were two undershot waterwheels, but only part of one survived
until the 1990s. The marks remain on the sides of the wheelpit. It
would appear that a small steam engine was installed after water
supply problems were encountered in the mid-1870s.

Each of the waterwheels worked two pairs of millstones, sack hoists
and grain and flour cleaners. The mill and its interior was restored in
1994 to a display condition. Although it is too fragile to work, the
machinery dating from the 1770s is unusually rare for being of all-
wooden construction. During archaeological investigations, an oak
post driven into the chalk bedrock was dated to between 1304 and
1494, not a very accurate date but it does accord with an early
mention of 'Wytemull' in historic documents in 1341. The miller's
house adjoins the mill on the road side, while the scene is completed
by the superb medieval White Mill Bridge which takes the road across
the Stour to Sturminster Marshall. White Mill is part of the Kingston
Lacy estate owned by the National Trust. Telephone: 01258 858051.

FURTHER READING

Addison, J. & Wailes, R., 'Dorset Watermills', Trans. Newcomen Soc., XXXV, 1962-3, 193-216

'Addendum to Dorset Watermills', Trans. Newcomen Soc., XXXVI, 1963-4, 175-181

Addison, J., 'Second Addendum to Dorset Watermills', Trans. Newcomen Soc., XLI, 1968-9, 139-162

Bone, M., 'Dorset Windmills', Somerset & Dorset Notes & Queries, XXI, March 1980, 11-19; March 1985, 430-1; Somerset & Dorset Notes & Queries, XXXIII, March 1995, 360-363

Bridges, S. & Papworth. M., 'Hogford Mill, Pamphill', Procs. Dorset Nat. Hist. & Arch. Soc., vol 114, 1992, 234-7

Dewar, H.S.L., 'The Windmills, Watermills and Horsemills of Dorset', Procs. Dorset Nat. Hist. & Arch. Soc., vol 82, 1960, 109-132

Eldred, K. & Papworth, M., 'West Mill, Corfe Castle', Proc. Dorset Nat. Hist. & Arch. Soc., vol 120, 1998, 63-68

Graham, A.H., 'The Old Malthouse, Abbotsbury, Dorset: The Medieval Watermill of the Benedictine Abbey', Procs. Dorset Nat. Hist. & Arch. Soc., vol 108, 1986, 103-125

Grace, N., 'White Mill, Shapwick', Procs. Dorset Nat. Hist. & Arch. Soc., vol 117, 1995, 135

Hodges, R., 'Excavation at Daws Mill', Procs. Dorset Nat. Hist. & Arch. Soc., vol 96, 1974, 19-44

James, J.F., 'Dorset Water Mills', Somerset & Dorset Notes & Queries, XXX, 1980, 419-20

Loosmore, P. & Clarke, R., Sturminster Newton Mill, Sturminster Newton Museum Booklet No. 6, 1995

Papworth, M., 'White Mill, Shapwick', Procs. Dorset Nat. Hist. & Arch. Soc., vol 115, 1993, 165

Papworth, M., Watts, M. et al, 'Watermills on the Kingston Lacy Estate, Dorset', Inds. Arch. Review, XVIII, No.1, 1995, 106-116

Pontain, R., Castleton Pumping Station: Sherborne. A History, Castleton Waterwheel Restoration Society, n.d.

Ross, M.S., 'The Mill House, Stour Provost, Dorset', Procs. Dorset Nat. Hist. & Arch. Soc., vol 117, 1995, 151-152

Watts, M., *Corn Milling*, Shire Publications, 1998

Watts, M., *Water and Wind Power*, Shire Publications, 2000.

ACKNOWLEDGEMENTS

I would especially like to thank my friend Martin Watts, millwright, for patiently fielding endless questions on the finer points of mills and milling. Mike Bone has given information from his researches on windmills and horsemills, and I am also appreciative of help from Jo Draper, Alan Graham, Michael Stoate, Tony Yoward, and the staffs of the Dorset County Museum, and Dorset County Reference Library, Dorchester.

Most of the photographs in the book are my own, but I am grateful to the following for allowing the inclusion of illustrations in their possession or for which they hold the copyright: Dorset County Museum; page 2 (also The Bridport Museum Service), 35, 38, 42, 44, 73: Martin Watts; 19, 24, 28, 58, and the drawings on pages 16, 22 and 23. The map on page 6 is by Christopher Chaplin and the illustrations on pages 18, 30, 43, 54, 55, 70 and 75 are from the Dovecote Press Collection.

The

DISCOVER DORSET

Series of Books

A series of paperback books providing informative illustrated
introductions to Dorset's history, culture and way of life.
The following titles have so far been published.

BRIDGES *David McFetrich and Jo Parsons*

CASTLES AND FORTS *Colin Pomeroy*

CRANBORNE CHASE *Desmond Hawkins*

FARMING *J.H.Bettey*

FOLLIES *Jonathan Holt*

FOSSILS *Richard Edmonds*

GEOLOGY *Paul Ensom*

THE GEORGIANS *Jo Draper*

THE INDUSTRIAL PAST *Peter Stanier*

ISLE OF PURBECK *Paul Hyland*

LEGENDS *Jeremy Harte*

MILLS *Peter Stanier*

PORTLAND *Stuart Morris*

POTTERY *Penny Copland-Griffiths*

THE PREHISTORIC AGE *Bill Putnam*

REGENCY, RIOT AND REFORM *Jo Draper*

THE ROMANS *Bill Putnam*

SAXONS AND VIKINGS *David Hinton*

SHIPWRECKS *Maureen Attwooll*

STONE QUARRYING *Jo Thomas*

THE VICTORIANS *Jude James*

All the books about Dorset published by The Dovecote Press
are available in bookshops throughout the county,
or in case of difficulty direct from the publishers.
The Dovecote Press Ltd, Stanbridge,
Wimborne, Dorset BH21 4JD
Tel: 01258 840549 www.dovecotepress.com